Horrid Henry's

Annual 2018

Horrid Henry's Annual 2018

Francesca Simon
Illustrated by Tony Ross

Orion
Children's Books

ORION CHILDREN'S BOOKS

First published in Great Britain in 2017
by Hodder and Stoughton

1 3 5 7 9 10 8 6 4 2

Compiled by Sally Byford from the Horrid Henry books
by Francesca Simon & illustrated by Tony Ross

A CIP catalogue record for this book
is available from the British Library.

ISBN 978 1 5101 0170 8

Printed and bound in China

The paper and board used in this book are from
well-managed forests and other responsible sources.

FSC www.fsc.org
MIX
Paper from
responsible sources
FSC® C104740

Orion Children's Books
An imprint of
Hachette Children's Group
Part of Hodder and Stoughton
Carmelite House
50 Victoria Embankment
London EC4Y 0DZ

An Hachette UK Company
www.hachette.co.uk
www.hachettechildrens.co.uk
www.horridhenry.co.uk

Contents

Hey there, my brave, daring and fearless Purple Hand Gang Members!

How lucky are you – my new annual is absolutely packed with everything you need to know about the best club in the world, the Purple Hand Gang, and our deadly enemies, the Secret Club. Bah! Margaret and her minions will be defeated once and for all, when I put my top secret plans into action. Meanwhile, you can find out all about becoming a spy, top-secret unbreakable codes and a few unbeatable ways to squish your enemies.

Hurrah!

Long live the Purple Hand Gang!

Down with the Secret Club!

Henry

Spot the Purple Hand Prints

Horrid Henry has splattered Purple Hand prints all over the Annual. How many can you find?

All About the Purple Hand Gang

The Purple Hand Gang is the *best* club ever in the history of the universe! (Obviously, since it's MY club.)

Here's why:

My club has the YUMMIEST biscuits ever! Oh boy, I'm getting hungry just thinking about those Chocolate Fudge Chewies and Triple Choc Chip Marshmallow Chewies. In fact – phew, that's better. Just scoffed a HUGE handful. I've left the Skull and Crossbones biscuit tin empty, which is just as well, in case Margaret decided to raid. Ha Ha!

No girls allowed.

Our Password (shhhhhhh) is Smelly Toads.

Motto: Down with Girls.

Members: Apart from me, Lord High Majesty of the Purple Hand, there's my *best* friend Ralph.*

*Oh. Sometimes Mum makes me let Peter in. It's so unfair! Peter has his own stupid club. I don't see why he has to slime all over mine. BUT ... his title is Lord Worm, or Lord High Worm. Ha ha, Peter! And I always make him be the guard.

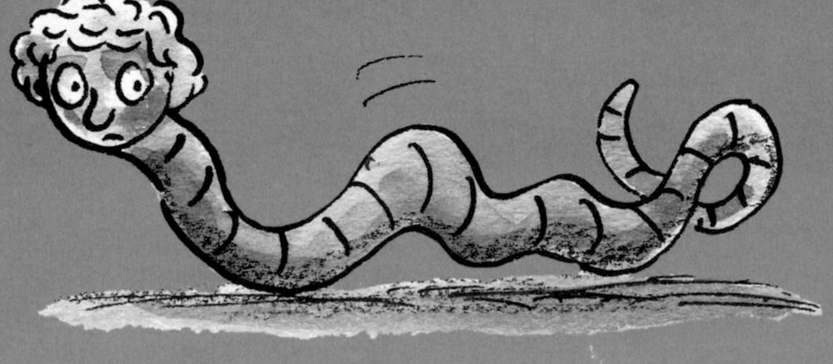

Secrets of the Secret Club

Margaret's pathetic club is called the 'Secret Club.'

But it's not very secret since I know everything about it. I know her password, where she hides her biscuits – in a tin under a blanket since you ask – and how her club members are ALWAYS quitting. So, my gang members, here's all you need to know to DESTROY the secret club.

Her not so top secret password is Nunga Nu.

The Mark of the Secret Club is a dagger.

Margaret likes to leave a drawing with a dagger behind when she tries to invade my den. But she will NEVER succeed!

Her copy-cat Motto: Down with Boys.

Members: Margaret, Susan, Linda and Gurinder.*

*But Margaret is such a mean bossy boots that her members leave her club. Which is handy for me because then they can become MY spies.

HORRID HENRY'S Tough Test

WARNING! THE BEST BOYS CLUB IS SMELLY!

So you want to join the Purple Hand Gang?
Take Horrid Henry's test and find out if he'll let you in
– or banish you to the Best Boys' Club!

1. Which of these is the best club rule?

a. No girls allowed!
b. No boys allowed!
c. Do a good deed every day.

2. What's your favourite plan to attack a rival gang?

a. Raid their biscuit tin and stinkbomb their den.
b. Set a booby trap and soak them all!
c. Let's all be friends and play nicely.

3. Choose your top two Stinky Stinkbomb ingredients?

a. Dead fish and rotten eggs.
b. Boys' smelly socks and dog poo.
c. Mummy's perfume and pretty flowers.

4. Which activities are the most fun?

a. Scoffing biscuits and beating the girls' gang.
b. Writing secret messages and spying on the boys' gang.
c. Doing good deeds and keeping the den neat and tidy.

5. What's your favourite stash of club grub?

a. Chocolate biscuits pinched from the girls' den – he he!
b. Chocolate fudge chewies sneaked from the boys' den – nah nah ne nah nah!
c. Carrot sticks and apples – so healthy and delicious.

6. How would you choose your club members?

a. They need a special skill, like burping – or bring plenty of sweets and other club grub.
b. They have to obey the leader at all times.
c. They should be tidy, spotless and well-behaved.

7. **What's the best sort of leader?**

a. Brave, clever, amazing.
b. Bossy, grouchy, mean.
c. Good, kind, helpful.

8. **A club member has been caught spying for the rival gang. What's the best punishment?**

a. Banishment for ever.
b. Never speaking to the sneaky spy again.
c. Hold a club meeting, and ask the spy to hand in their membership book and badge, and leave quietly.

Count up your number of a's, b's and c's. How did you do? Find out the verdict from Horrid Henry.

Mostly a's:

Well done! You're a winner! Welcome to the Purple Hand Gang! But remember – I'm the leader and you do as I say. And don't forget to bring loads of biscuits, crisps and fizzywizz with you, or I might change my mind.

Mostly b's:

It looks like you're a sneaky spy for Moody Margaret's Secret Club! So be warned – if you don't do exactly what that bossyboots tells you, you won't last long in her club. And you're not joining mine!

Mostly c's:

You sound like a telltale nappypants ninny, so you'll fit right in with Perfect Peter, Tidy Ted, Spotless Sam and Goody Goody Gordon, doing their good deeds in the soppy old Best Boys' Club. Yeuch!

Purple Hand Gang Wordsearch

Can you find all these words hidden in the puzzle?
Look up, down, across and diagonally.

d	c	e	e	d	g	s	d	f	s
f	i	o	s	n	w	a	l	h	p
a	s	n	m	e	o	z	l	c	a
m	d	r	e	i	[illegible]	r	t	f	r
r	a	[illegible]	s	y	e	[illegible]	h	e	t
d	r	u	v	u	s	e	d	r	r
e	o	[illegible]	[illegible]	p	c	o	t	r	e
u	k	[illegible]	o	o	c	s	e	g	g
[illegible]	b	m	o	b	k	n	i	t	s
p	a	r	s	w	o	r	d	b	s

biscuits
code
comics
crisps
fizzywizz
flag
fort
motto
password
stinkbomb
sweets
throne
traps

When you've found all the words, write the leftover letters in the spaces below. You'll discover which smells Henry uses in the stinkbomb he makes to attack the Secret Club.

_ _ _ _ _ _ _ _ _ _ _ _ _ _ _ _

_ _ _ _ _ _ _ _ _ _ _ _ _ _ _

The answers are on page 58.

HORRID HENRY'S Stinkbomb

Horrid Henry rubbed his hands. This was fantastic! At last, he had a spy in the enemy's camp! He'd easily defend himself against that stupid stinkbomb. Margaret would only let it off when he was in the fort. His sentry would be on the lookout armed with a goo-shooter. When Margaret tried to sneak in with her stinkbomb – ker-pow!

"Hang on a sec," said Horrid Henry, "why should I trust you?"

"Because Margaret is mean and horrible, and I hate her," said Susan.

"So from now on," said Horrid Henry, "you're working for me."

Susan wasn't sure she liked the sound of that. Then she remembered Margaret's mean cackle.

"Okay," said the traitor.

Peter sneaked into his garden and collided with someone.

"Ouch!" said Peter.

"Watch where you're going!" snapped Susan.

They glared at each other suspiciously.

"What were you doing at Margaret's?" said Susan.

"Nothing," said Peter. "What were you doing at my house?"

"Nothing," said Susan.

Peter walked towards Henry's fort, whistling.

Susan walked towards Margaret's tent, whistling.

Well, if Susan was spying on Henry for Margaret, Peter certainly wasn't going to warn him. Serve Henry right.

Well, if Peter was spying on Margaret for Henry, Susan certainly wasn't going to warn her. Serve Margaret right.

Dungeon Drinks, eh?

Margaret liked that idea much better than her stinkbomb plot.

"I've changed my mind about the stinkbomb," said Margaret. "I'm going to swap his drinks for Dungeon Drink stinkers instead."

"Good idea," said Lazy Linda. "Less work!"

Stinkbomb, eh?

Henry liked that much better than his dungeon drink plot. Why hadn't he thought of that himself?

"I've changed my mind about the Dungeon Drinks," said Henry. "I'm going to stinkbomb her instead."

"Yeah," said Rude Ralph. "When?"

"Now," said Horrid Henry. "Come on, let's go to my room."

Which club comes out on top in the end? Find out in *Horrid Henry's Stinkbomb*.

Creepy-Crawly Cookies

To stop Moody Margaret and Sour Susan sneaking off with the Purple Hand's grub, Horrid Henry turns his cookies into blood-curdling creepy-crawlies!

You will need:

- round, sandwich-style chocolate biscuits
- liquorice laces – black or red
- sugar-coated chocolate sweets
- a tube of ready-made icing

Instructions

1. Make the spider legs by cutting up a liquorice lace into eight pieces approximately 4 centimetres long.
2. Squeeze a dot of icing on the end of each leg, and push them all between the two sandwich biscuit layers.
3. Add evil eyes by sticking two sugar-coated chocolate sweets on top of your biscuit using the tube of ready-made icing.
4. Leave the icing to harden.
5. Carefully put the spiders into your club cookie tin.

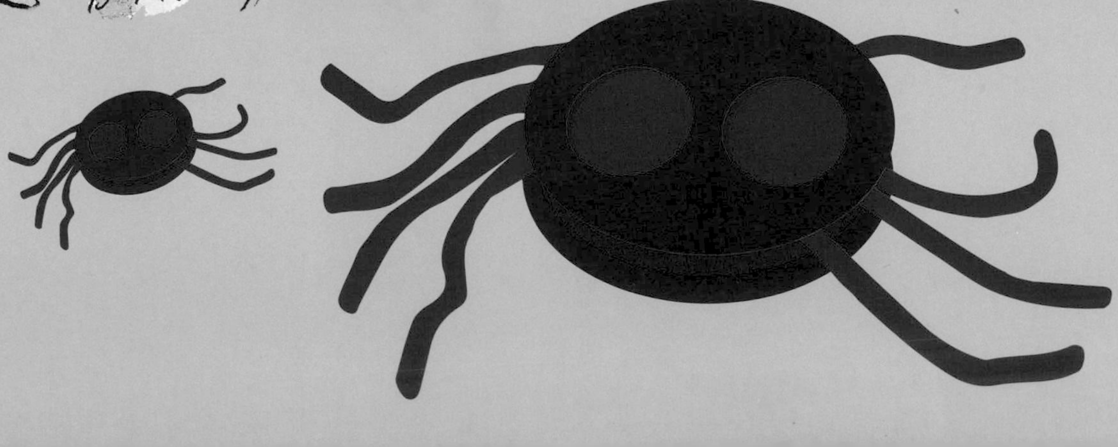

Who Comes Next?

Solve the pattern puzzles by working out who comes next in each sequence. Draw a picture in each box or write the letter a, b, c or d, as shown below.

a b c d

Check out the answers on page 58.

Purple Hand Gang Plans

Our plans are simple – to take over the world! But first we have to spy on our rivals, and thwart any dastardly plans they have to booby-trap our club. Next, we have to make stinkbombs and booby-trap the Secret Club. I like using my Dungeon Drink Kit to make horrid potions to trick mean Margaret.

PURPLE HAND PLANS

- Steal the Secret Club flag
- Steal the Secret Club biscuits
- Booby-trap the Secret Club den
- Get Susan to spy for us
- Write our own newspaper, *The Basher*

Secret Club Plans

SECRET CLUB PLANS

- Steal the Purple Hand Gang flag
- Steal the Purple Hand Gang biscuits
- Booby-trap the Purple Hand den
- Get Peter to spy for us
- Write our own newspaper, *The Daily Dagger*.

Would You Make a Good Spy?

Could you be Chief Spy for the Purple Hand? Check out your spying skills – and find out! First, look at this birthday party picture for two minutes. Then cover it up and answer the questions on the next page.

NO PEEPING!

1. Whose birthday party is it?

2. What party game is Beefy Bert playing?

3. Who is holding a Supersoaker Water Blaster 2000?

4. What is Greedy Graham eating?

5. Where is Anxious Andrew hiding?

6. Is Weepy William crying?

7. What sort of food is there on the table?

8. What is Horrid Henry standing on?

9. As well as Horrid Henry, Greedy Graham, Anxious Andrew, Beefy Bert and Weepy William, there are two other guests? Who are they?

BONUS QUESTION
Be honest! How many times did you sneak a peek back at the picture?!

Now check the picture or the answers on page 58 to find your score. How did you do?

7-9: A champion score – you'd make a super sneaky spy!
4-6: Not bad – but you need to be nosier!
0-3: Call yourself a spy? You're sacked!

Stinkbomb Sudoku

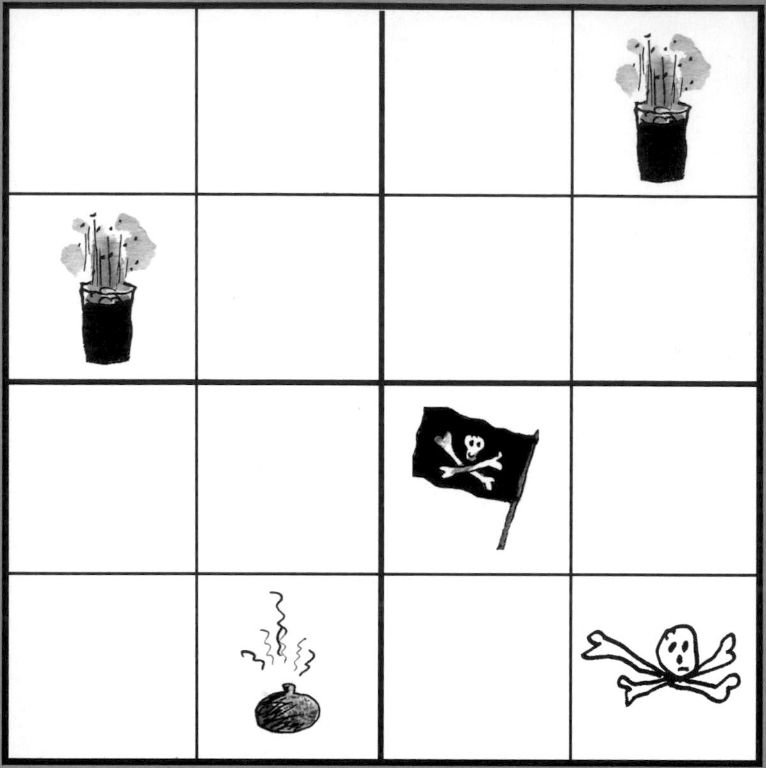

Fill in the sudoku so that every square, row and column contains a picture of a stinkbomb, a dungeon drink, a pirate flag, and a skull and crossbones.

Try a trickier one!
Fill in every square and row with numbers 1-6.

2		5	3		4
	6			2	
1					2
5					1
	5			1	
6			2		3

TOP TIP:
First fill in all the 1's, and then the 2's.

The answers are on page 58.

Missing Words Crossword

Find the missing words from the list below to complete the crossword clues. Clue 4 Down has been filled in to get you started.

sand	fang	cakes	**pants**√	bed
man	boom	meat	baby	sleep

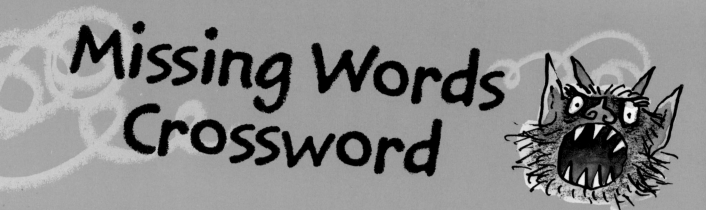

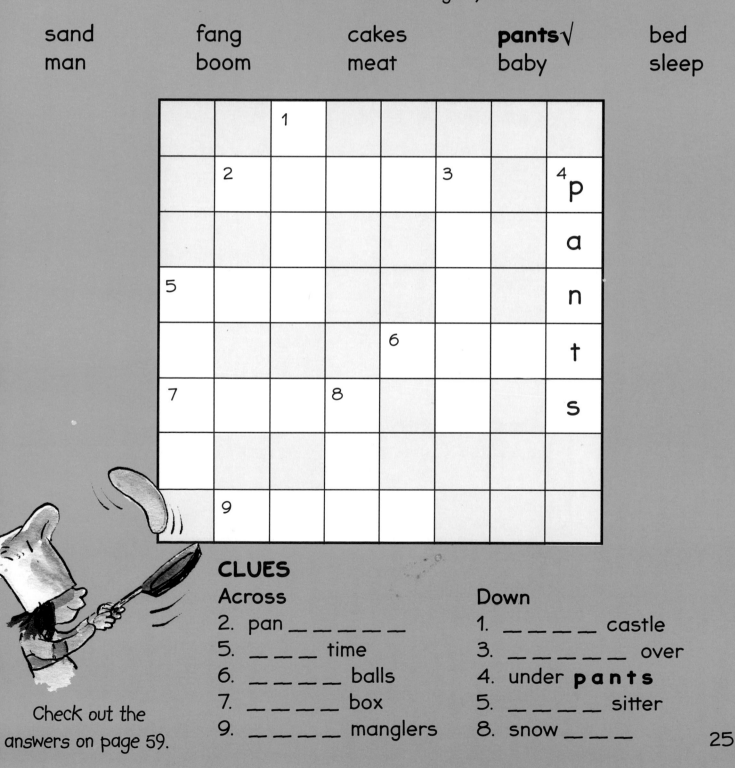

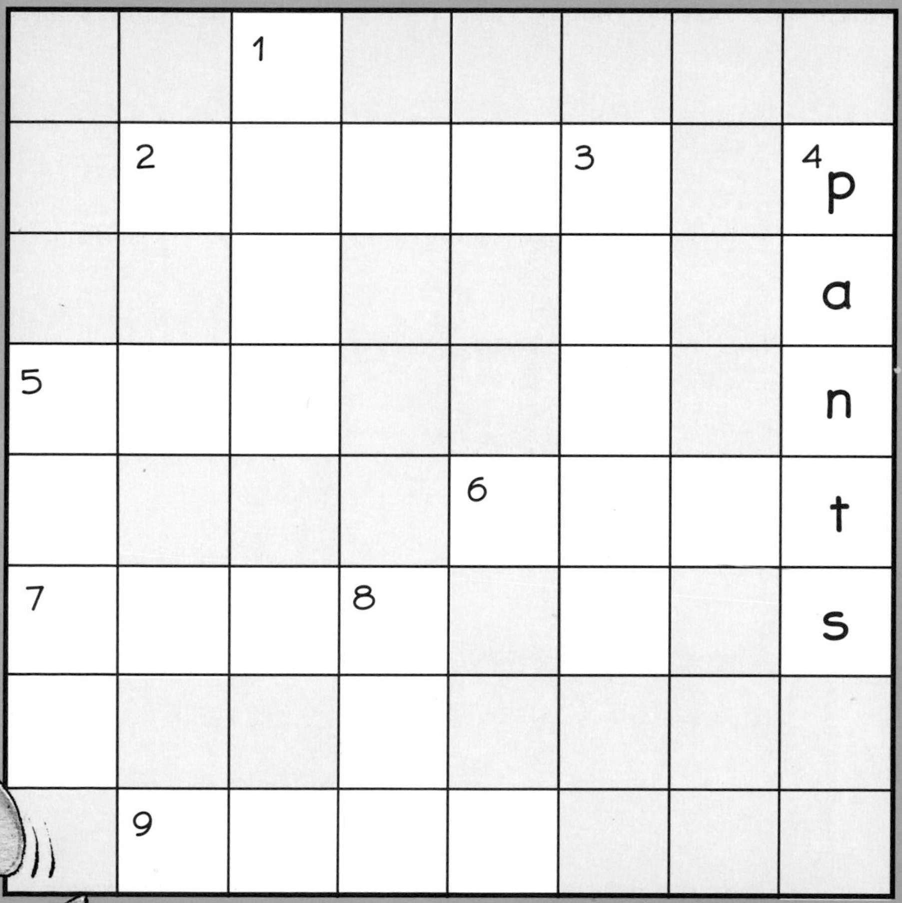

CLUES

Across

2. pan _ _ _ _ _ _
5. _ _ _ time
6. _ _ _ _ _ balls
7. _ _ _ _ _ box
9. _ _ _ _ _ manglers

Down

1. _ _ _ _ _ castle
3. _ _ _ _ _ _ _ over
4. under **p a n t s**
5. _ _ _ _ _ sitter
8. snow _ _ _

Check out the answers on page 59.

Horrid Henry's Cunning Code

The Purple Hand Gang keep their plans top secret by using Horrid Henry's cunning code. Start with the yellow column and find the answers in the orange column. But Henry needs to watch out – there's a double-crossing spy sneaking about. Whose side is he on?

a	c
b	d
c	e
d	f
e	g
f	h
g	i
h	j
i	k
j	l
k	m
l	n
m	o
n	p
o	q
p	r
q	s
r	t
s	u
t	v
u	w
v	x
w	y
x	z
y	a
z	b

vqr ugetgv ura tgrqtv

c uvcuj qh ejqeqncvg jcu dggp jkffgp kp vjg ugetgv enwd vgpv.

Peter's code to Henry says:

wtigpv!

enwd itwd tckf vqfca! Oggv cv vjg hqtv chvgt uejqqn.

Henry's code to Ralph says:

MOODY MARGARET'S Unbreakable Code

Moody Margaret thinks Horrid Henry's code is dumb. Her own Secret Club code is unbreakable – unless you sneak a peek at the codebreaker! Decode the messages and discover who gobbled up the chocolate in the end!

a	b	c	d	e	f	g	h	i	j	k	l	m
✓	◗	♎	★	●	≋	Ø	›	∏	‹	☒	▲	◆
n	**o**	**p**	**q**	**r**	**s**	**t**	**u**	**v**	**w**	**x**	**y**	**z**
↘	⊖	⍓	□	∑	«	☹	∞	✕	■	•	▼	✚

■✓∑↘∏↘Ø! ☹›●
⍓∞∑⍓▲● ›✓↘★
■∏▲▲ ∑✓∏★
☹⊖↘∏Ø›☹.

Peter's code to Margaret says:

□∞∏♎☒! «■✓⍓ ⊖∞∑
♎›⊖♎⊖▲✓☹● ■∏☹› ☹›●
◆✓∑☒ ⊖≋ ☹›● ★✓ØØ●∑.
⍓●☹●∑ ∏« ♎›∏●≋ «⍓▼
↘⊖■. ↘⊖☹ ▼⊖∞.

Margaret's code to Susan says:

⊖☒ ◗⊖««▼◗⊖⊖☹«!
☹›● ♎›⊖♎⊖▲✓☹●
■✓« ▼∞◆◆▼. ↘✓›
↘✓› ↘● ↘✓› ↘✓›.

Susan's code to Margaret says:

The answers are on page 59.

Pirate Kit Criss-cross

Horrid Henry wants to sneak Moody Margaret's Pirate Kit for the Purple Hand Gang. Can you find all the amazing things it contains in the criss-cross below?

TOP TIP:
Fill in all 5-letter words last.

3 letters
hat

4 letters
hook

5 letters
sword
sabre
chest
skull

6 letters
dagger

7 letters
cutlass

8 letters
eyepatch

10 letters
crossbones

Match the Flags

Moody Margaret, Sour Susan, Lazy Linda, Singing Soraya and Gorgeous Gurinder have all painted a Secret Club dagger flag. From the 25 flags below, can you find their matching flag?

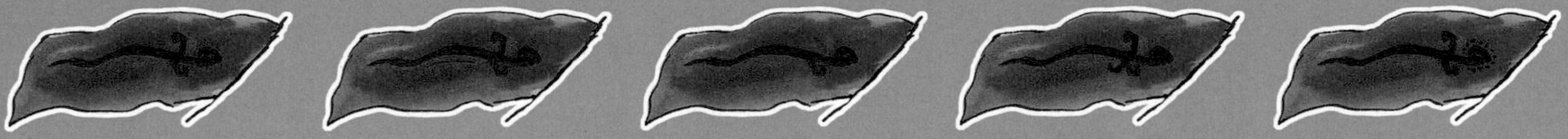

Moody Margaret	Sour Susan	Lazy Linda	Singing Soraya	Gorgeous Gurinder
FLAG	FLAG	FLAG	FLAG	FLAG

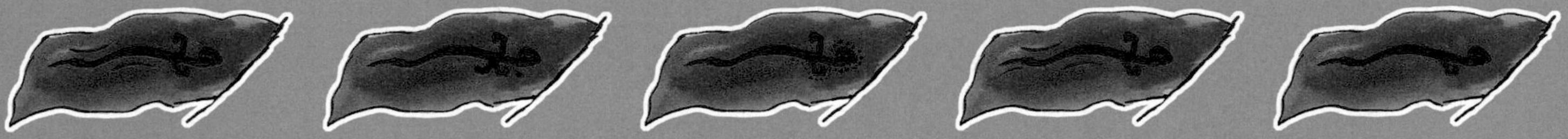

1 2 3 4 5

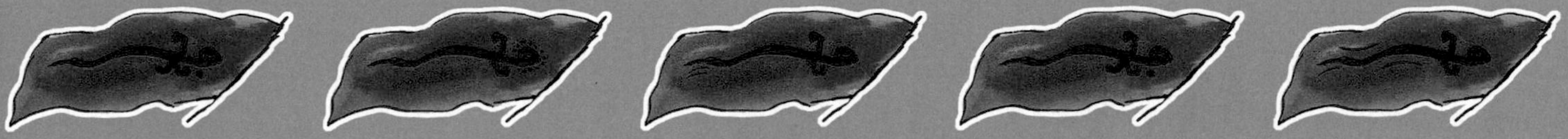

6 7 8 9 10

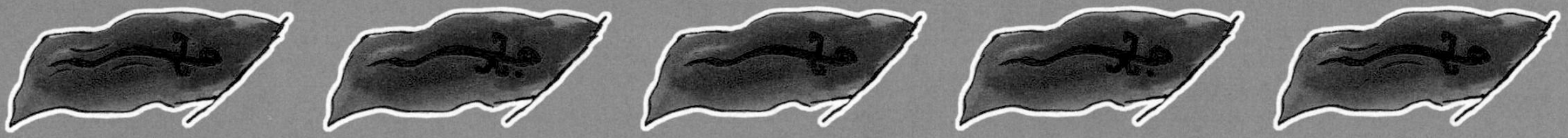

11 12 13 14 15

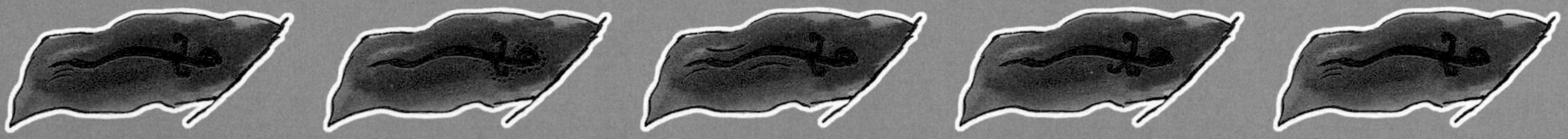

16 17 18 19 20

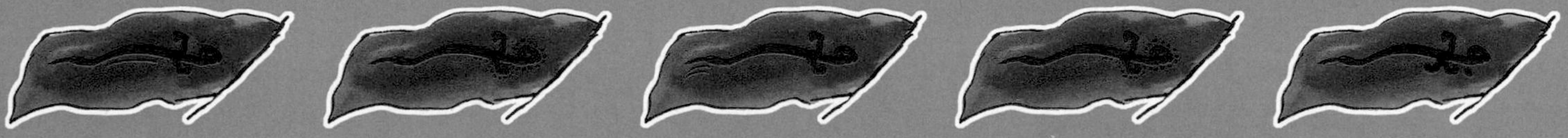

21 22 23 24 25

The answers are on page 59.

Can You Keep a Secret?

If you want to join the Purple Hand Gang, you have to be good at keeping secrets. Take the quiz and see if you are.

1. You receive a note in the club's secret code. After you've read and remembered the message, what do you do with the note?

a. Tear it into tiny pieces and pop it in the dustbin.
b. Screw it into a ball and sling it in the wastepaper basket.
c. Leave it lying around on your bedroom floor.

2. When you want to enter the club den, how do you say the secret password?

a. In a quiet whisper.
b. In your normal voice.
c. As loudly as you can.

3. How do you remember the club's secret codebreaker?

a. Fold it up and hide it in your secret drawer.
b. Keep it safe in an envelope marked, 'KEEP OUT! CLUB CODEBREAKER'.
c. Pin it up on your bedroom wall.

4. Do you know how to write an invisible note?

a. Write in lemon juice.
b. Use a white felt tip pen.
c. I dunno.

5. What's the best way to pass on an important piece of information to your friend – like where the rival gang hide their chocolate biscuits?

a. Send a secret note in code.
b. Tell your friend in the school playground – and hope no one else is listening.
c. Make your little brother or sister go and tell your friend.

6. What's the best hiding place for a secret note in your bedroom?

a. Tucked into a tiny hole in the side of your teddy.
b. In your pants drawer.
c. Under the pillow.

7. **You're sneaking a packet of biscuits out to your club den. How do you get them there without being spotted?**

a. Carry a large toy and hide them behind it.
b. Stick them down the front of your jumper.
c. Hide them behind your back.

8. **Your gang has planned an attack on the rival club – but it's your tea time. How do you escape your parents to join in the attack?**

a. Tell them you're not feeling very well and need to go to bed, then sneak out through the back door.
b. Say you've heard a funny noise in the garden and you're going to investigate.
c. Tell them you don't want any tea because you've got to go and attack your rival club.

How did you do? Count up your number of a's, b's and c's.

Mostly a's:

You're a super-sneaky secret keeper! The Purple Hand Gang's plans would be safe with you – and you'd always be there to help carry out the attacks.

Mostly b's:

You keep some secrets safe – but let others slip out by mistake. Remember – always whisper so enemy ears don't hear, and check out some hiding places where your mum won't look!

Mostly c's:

You're either shouting out secret passwords or posting up club codes for everyone to see. You're a great big blabbermouth and secrets are never safe with you around!

BE WARNED!!
If you're a telltale, the Purple Hand will strike!

You'll be drenched in icy cold water, forced to walk the plank and exiled to an island with no TV.

Tricking the Enemy

Moody Margaret and Sour Susan dare the Purple Hand Gang to eat a big bowl of wiggly worms. What Henry and Ralph don't know is that the worms are made of jelly!

To Make Wiggly Worms . . .

You will need:

- a tall glass or jar
- bendy plastic straws – enough to fill your container
- a pack of pink jelly
- 4 sheets of gelatine
- 2 tablespoons of double cream
- a jug
- a large bowl

Instructions

1. Pack the straws tightly into the jar or glass, so that they are standing up on end.
2. Ask a grown-up to make up the pink jelly for you in a jug.
3. Mix in 4 sheets of gelatine and stir until they have dissolved.
4. Let the jelly cool a bit.
5. Stir in 2 tablespoons of double cream.
6. Place your jar of straws into a big bowl – to catch any spilt jelly!

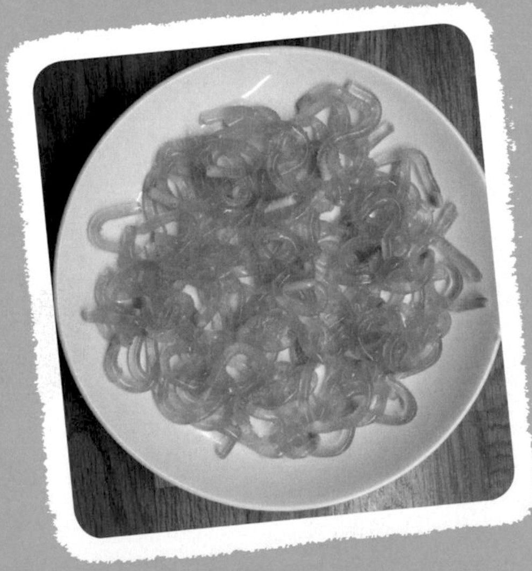

7. Carefully pour the jelly mixture from the jug into the straws.
8. Stop pouring when the jelly mixture reaches almost to the top of the jar.
9. Put the jelly in the fridge overnight.
10. Next day, slowly squeeze each of your pink jelly worms out of its straw – and let them slither into a bowl or plate.

Horrid Henry and Rude Ralph are furious!
But they soon get their own back on the Secret Club –
with their exploding bags . . .

To Make a Big Bang Bag . . .

You will need:

- 4 teaspoons of bicarbonate of soda
- a tissue
- ½ cup vinegar
- a self-seal sandwich bag

Instructions

1. Put 4 rounded teaspoons of bicarbonate of soda into the middle of the tissue.
2. Fold up the tissue like a little parcel, so that the bicarbonate of soda is safely wrapped up inside.
3. Pour the vinegar into the sandwich bag.
4. Pop the parcel of bicarbonate of soda into the sandwich bag, and quickly seal it up.
5. Shake the bag up until it starts to fizz …

   … then it's time for action. Horrid Henry flings the bag into the Secret Club tent … and BANG!

WARNING!
Don't make an exploding bag in the house – your parents will make you eat sprouts every day for a year and ban TV forever.

Dash to the Dens Maze

HORRID HENRY – GO!

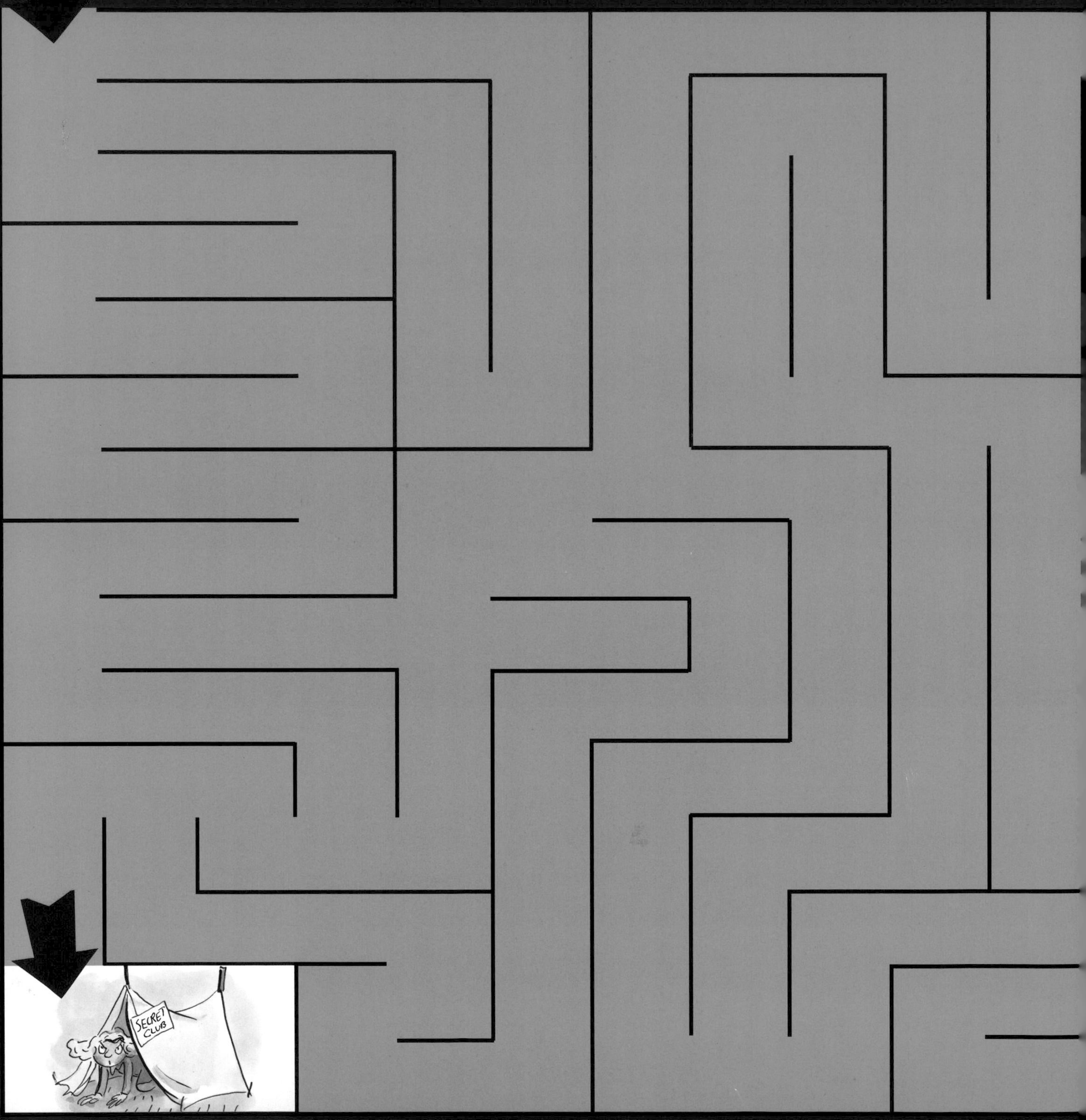

Help Horrid Henry reach the Purple Hand Fort and Moody Margaret find the Secret Club tent – by the shortest routes possible.
BEWARE – if you lead them down the wrong path, they could end up at their arch-rival's den!

MOODY MARGARET – GO!

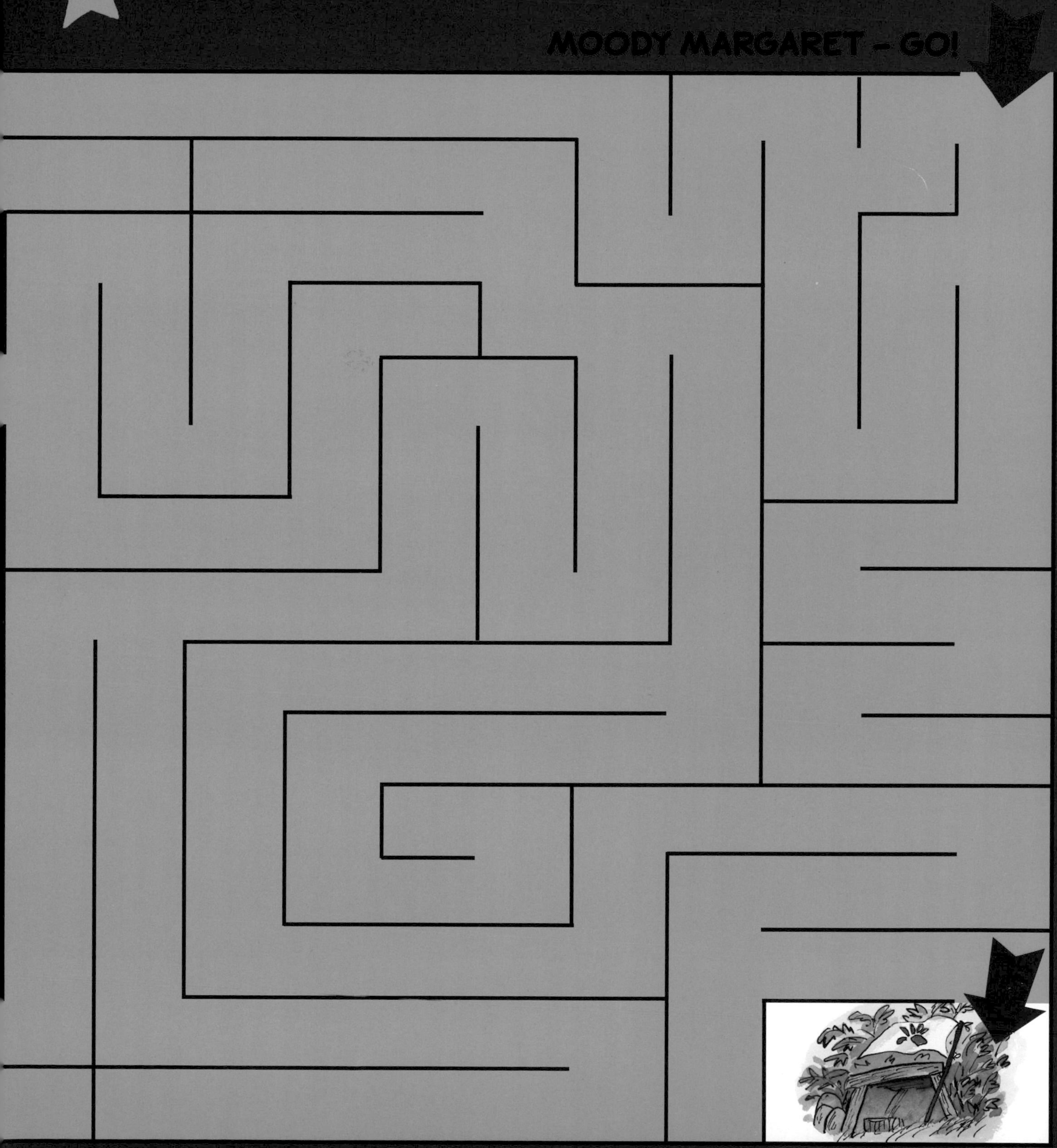

Check out the answers on page 60.

HORRID HENRY and the Secret Club

"Halt! Who goes there?"

"Me."

"Who's me?" said Moody Margaret.

"ME!" said Sour Susan.

"What's the password?"

"Uhhhh … " Sour Susan paused. What was the password? She thought and thought and thought.

"Potatoes?"

Margaret sighed loudly. Why was she friends with such a stupid person?

"No, it isn't."

"Yes, it is," said Susan.

"Potatoes was last week's password," said Margaret.

"No, it wasn't."

"Yes, it was," said Moody Margaret. "It's my club and I decide."

There was a very long pause.

"All right," said Susan sourly. "What is the password?"

"I don't know if I'm going to tell you," said Margaret. "I could be giving away a big secret to the enemy."

"But I'm not the enemy," said Susan. "I'm Susan."

"Shhhh!" said Margaret. "We don't want Henry to find out who's in the secret club."

Susan looked quickly over her shoulder. The enemy was nowhere to be seen. She whistled twice.

"All clear," said Sour Susan. "Now, please let me in."

Moody Margaret thought for a moment. Letting someone in without the password broke the first club rule.

"Prove to me you're Susan, and not the enemy pretending to be Susan," said Margaret.

"You know it's me," wailed Susan.

"Prove it."

Susan stuck her foot into the tent.

"I'm wearing the black patent leather shoes with the blue flowers I always wear."

"No good," said Margaret. "The enemy could be a master of disguise."

Susan stamped her foot. "And I know that you were the one who pinched Helen and I'm going to tell Miss …"

"Come closer to the tent flap," said Margaret.

Susan bent over.

"Now listen to me," said Margaret. "Because I'm only going to tell you once …"

Does Moody Margaret ever let Sour Susan into the Secret Club tent? Find out in *Horrid Henry and the Secret Club*.

Dungeon Drinks

Horrid Henry loves to gross-out his family
by guzzling up these dungeon drinks.
They look gruesome – but they taste good!

Bibble Babble Drink

You will need:

- cola
- black food colouring (optional)
- vanilla ice cream

Instructions

1. Fill a glass with cola.
2. Add a few drops of black food colouring.
3. Put a big blob of ice cream on the top.
4. Dribble a bit more cola on top of the ice cream.

Enjoy!

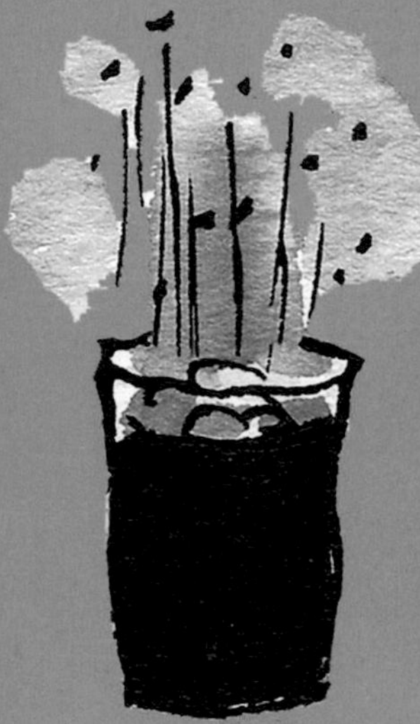

Slimy Lime

You will need:

- fizzy lemonade or limeade
- green food colouring
- tube of sherbet

Instructions

1. Put all the sherbet in the bottom of your glass.
2. Fill up the glass with lemonade or limeade.
3. Add a few drops of green food colouring.

Watch it bubble and froth!

What Makes a Great Leader?

A great leader tells his minions what to do.

A great leader makes sure all the biscuits are HIS.

A great leader makes sure no worms belong to his gang.

A great leader has the best top secret plans to DEFEAT the enemy.

A great leader knows EVERYTHING about stinkbombs and booby traps and how to trick evil enemies.

A great leader builds the best club house and has the best flag.

Which is why I, Henry, am Lord High Majesty of the Purple Hand Gang, the greatest club ever in the history of the universe, and Margaret is stuck with the so-called Secret Club. Member of the Secret Club: Only Margaret, because no one wants to be with such a frog face bossy boots.

Would You Make a Great Leader?

Follow this flowchart and find out
if you've got what it takes to be great . . .

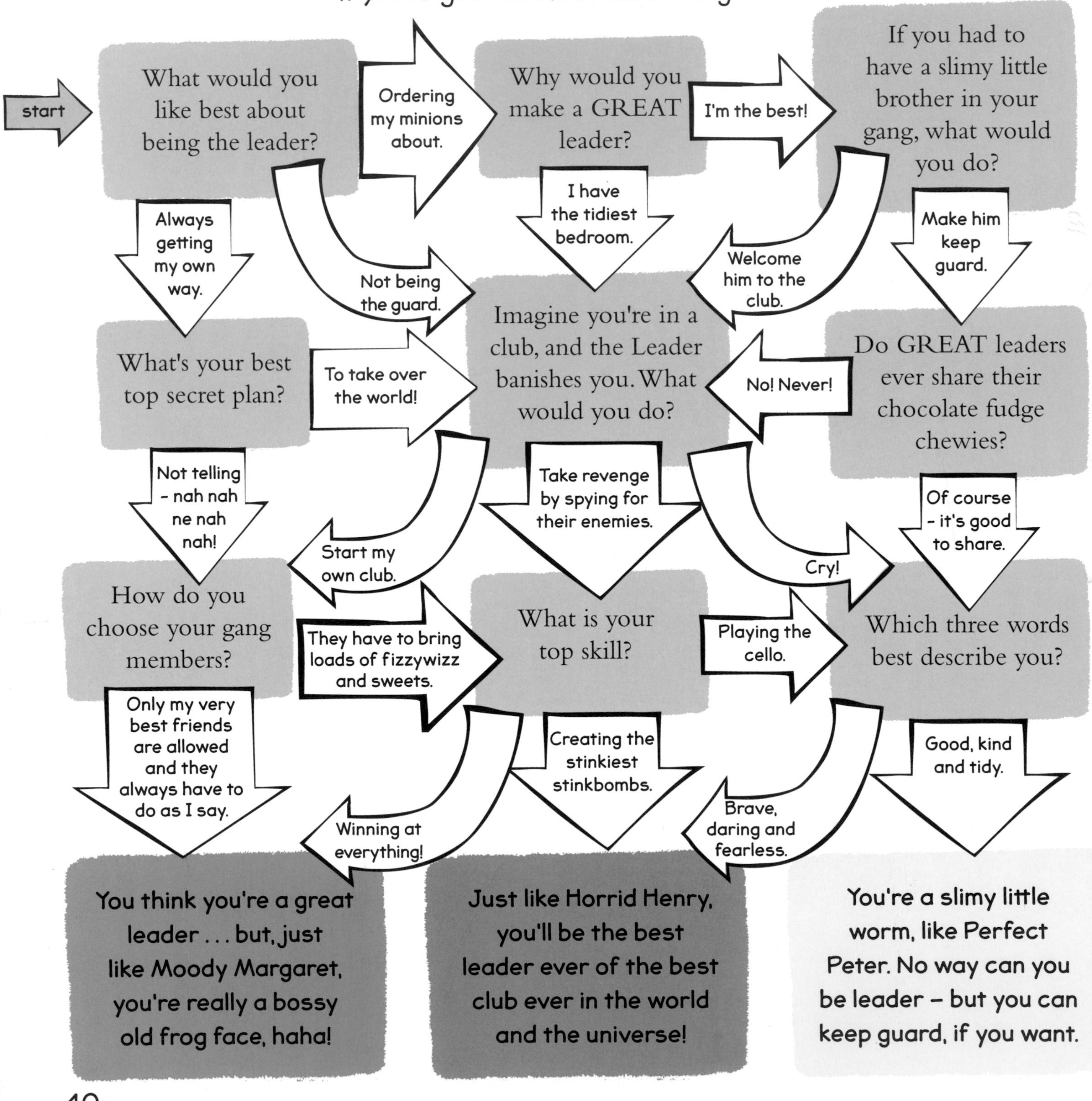

start
What would you like best about being the leader?
Ordering my minions about.
Why would you make a GREAT leader?
I'm the best!
If you had to have a slimy little brother in your gang, what would you do?
Always getting my own way.
Not being the guard.
I have the tidiest bedroom.
Welcome him to the club.
Make him keep guard.
What's your best top secret plan?
To take over the world!
Imagine you're in a club, and the Leader banishes you. What would you do?
No! Never!
Do GREAT leaders ever share their chocolate fudge chewies?
Not telling - nah nah ne nah nah!
Start my own club.
Take revenge by spying for their enemies.
Cry!
Of course - it's good to share.
How do you choose your gang members?
They have to bring loads of fizzywizz and sweets.
What is your top skill?
Playing the cello.
Which three words best describe you?
Only my very best friends are allowed and they always have to do as I say.
Winning at everything!
Creating the stinkiest stinkbombs.
Brave, daring and fearless.
Good, kind and tidy.
You think you're a great leader . . . but, just like Moody Margaret, you're really a bossy old frog face, haha!
Just like Horrid Henry, you'll be the best leader ever of the best club ever in the world and the universe!
You're a slimy little worm, like Perfect Peter. No way can you be leader – but you can keep guard, if you want.

Password Puzzle

Perfect Peter tries to guess the passwords for the Purple Hand and the Secret Club, so he can sneak in and spy on both camps. Can you find all the words he guesses in the puzzle below? The words go backwards, forwards, up and down.

poopsicle
dagger
basher
burp
spitballs
ketchup
pancakes
gotcha
skeleton
spiders
trumpet
zombies
fangmangler

t	s	r	s	m	f	p	p	z	e
r	g	e	l	l	a	a	o	o	l
u	o	g	l	r	n	n	o	m	n
m	t	g	a	e	g	c	p	b	o
p	c	a	b	h	m	a	s	i	t
e	h	d	t	s	a	k	i	e	e
t	a	y	i	a	n	e	c	s	l
b	u	r	p	b	g	s	l	t	e
o	a	d	s	s	l	n	e	u	k
p	u	h	c	t	e	k	n	g	s
s	p	i	d	e	r	s	a	n	u

The leftover letters spell out the correct passwords – fit them into the spaces below.

The Purple Hand password is: _ _ _ _ _ _ _ _ _ _ _ _ _

The Secret Club password is: _ _ _ _ _ _ _ _

The answers are on page 60.

Purple Hand Gang versus Secret Club Bingo

You will need:

- 2 players plus one caller
- 1 Purple Hand Gang Card
- 1 Secret Club Card
- 12 small pieces of paper
- a box, bowl or hat
- 6 counters or coins

Purple Hand Gang Card

Secret Club Card

Instructions

1. Make your own Purple Hand Gang and Secret Club cards by copying or photocopying the cards shown below.
2. On each of the 12 small pieces of paper draw – or write the name of – one of the pictures that appear on the cards. Fold up the pieces of paper and put them all in a box, bowl or hat and give them a good shake to mix them up.
3. Give one player the Purple Hand Gang card and the other player the Secret Club card. Each player has 6 counters or coins.
4. The caller takes a piece of paper from the hat and calls it out. If that picture is on your card, cover it with a counter.
5. The first player to cover all 6 pictures on their card is the winner.

Snail Trail Tangled Strings

How do snails get their shells so shiny?
By using snail varnish!

The Purple Hand Gang, the Secret Club and the Best Boys are holding a Snail Race. Follow the slime trails and find out which club comes 1st, 2nd and 3rd.

Why did the snail cross the road?
I don't know, but will let you know when it gets here!

Write your answers in the spaces above and go to page 60 to see if you're right.

Garden Games

It's all-out war when the Purple Hand Gang and the Secret Club compete in the Garden Games. Get your own gang together, take on your arch-rivals – and win!

Who Can Blow the Loudest Trumpet?

Moody Margaret believes she'll be the best – until she finds out that the trumpet is a blade of grass!

You will need:

- a wide blade of grass

Instructions

1. Rinse your blade of grass with water to make sure it's clean.
2. With your fingernail, make a hole down the middle of the grass.
3. Put your thumbs on either side of the grass and press them together – so there's a small gap between your thumbs and the grass is stretched tightly in-between them.
4. Take a big breath and blow in-between your thumbs. The grass vibrates … and makes a loud noise like a trumpet. The loudest wins!

Chilly T-Shirts

A team race to pull on t-shirts – to be played outside on a hot, sunny day!

You will need:

- two teams
- one t-shirt for each team member
- a freezer
- plastic bags

Instructions

1. Soak all the t-shirts in water, then squeeze out as much water as you can.
2. Put each t-shirt in a separate plastic bag and put them all in the freezer overnight.
3. When you're ready to play, take the t-shirts out of the freezer.
4. Shout: Ready, Steady, Go! And the race is on for each team to defrost and pull on all their t-shirts.

Fishing for Fizzywizz

When the prize is a can of fizzywizz, Horrid Henry is desperate to win.

You will need:

- a key or another small metal object
- a piece of string about 3 metres long
- a stick about 1 metre long
- a can of fizzy drink

Instructions

1. Make your fishing rod. Tie the key very firmly to one end of the string. Tie the other end of the string securely to one end of the stick. Ask an adult to help you to make sure the key can't come loose and fly off.
2. Place the can of drink at a distance from the fisherman – as far away as the length of the string.
3. Take it in turns to try and throw the key onto the can – using your rod with a casting action like a fisherman.
4. The first person to hit the can with the key wins the fizzy drink.
5. **WARNING:** Keep well out of the way when the fisherman is casting so you don't get hit by the key.

Hunting for Treasure

Hunting for treasure is easy – unless you're blindfolded!

You will need:

- two teams
- two blindfolds
- hidden treasure

Instructions

1. One player from each team is blindfolded.
2. The other players hide the treasure.
3. The blindfolded players are spun around.
4. Now the fun starts! Each team works together to be the first to find the treasure. The blindfolded player sets off, and their team players shout 'hot' if he is heading in the right direction, and 'cold' if he is going the wrong way. This game can get very noisy – especially when Moody Margaret is screaming!
5. 'Hot' and 'cold' are the only words allowed.
6. The first blindfolded player to reach the treasure wins for their team.

Make a Pirate Hat

Here's how to make your own pirate hat, just like Moody Margaret's.

You will need:

- a sheet of newspaper or a piece of A3 black paper or card
- white paper
- a black crayon, a felt tip pen or paint
- glue
- sticky tape

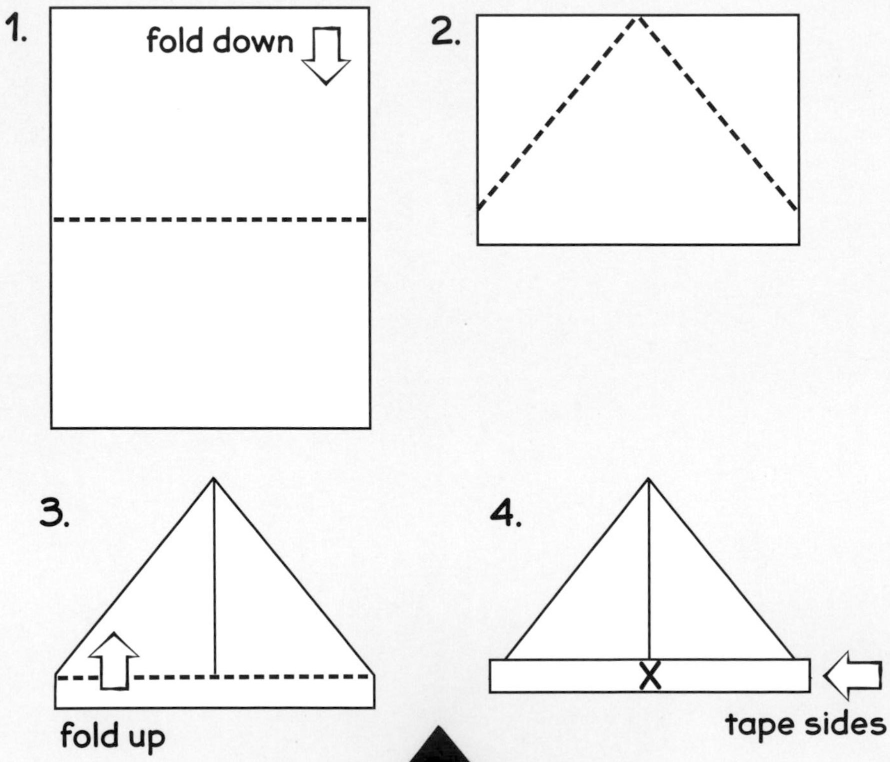

Instructions

1. Fold the piece of paper in half.
2. Fold in the top corners to make a triangle, leaving a small strip at the bottom.
3. Fold up the bottom strip, then turn over and fold up the strip on the other side.
4. Tape the sides to make the hat stronger.
5. Draw or paint a skull and crossbones on the white paper. Cut it out and stick it onto the front of the hat.

Club Crossword

You can find all the answers to the crossword clues in the picture!

CLUES

	1			2			
3		4					5
			6			7	
		8					

Across

1. Who is spying on the Secret Club through a telescope?
3. Which boy is wearing a brown jumper?
6. Who is waving the Secret Club flag?
8. What is Moody Margaret holding?

Down

2. What kind of hats are Henry, Ralph and Margaret wearing?
3. The colour of Sour Susan's skirt?
4. What is Rude Ralph wearing round his neck?
5. What is Perfect Peter carrying?
7. What is the colour of the Secret Club flag?

The answers are on page 60.

BRAINY BRIAN'S Big Quiz

It's time to brainstorm Brainy Brian's Big Quiz. Read each statement below and tick if you think it's TRUE or FALSE.

1. Perfect Peter's teacher is called Miss Ugly.

   TRUE ☐ FALSE ☐

2. Horrid Henry's hobby is collecting Gizmos from Sweet Tweet cereal boxes.

   TRUE ☐ FALSE ☐

3. Moody Margaret's mum calls her My Little Maggie Moo.

   TRUE ☐ FALSE ☐

4. Rude Ralph never forgets to say 'please' and 'thank you'.

   TRUE ☐ FALSE ☐

5. Horrid Henry's favourite vegetables are sprouts.

   TRUE ☐ FALSE ☐

6. Miss Battle-Axe loves football.

   TRUE ☐ FALSE ☐

7. Sour Susan was chosen to present flowers to the Queen.

   TRUE ☐ FALSE ☐

8. Perfect Peter loves a nice, hot bath.

   TRUE ☐ FALSE ☐

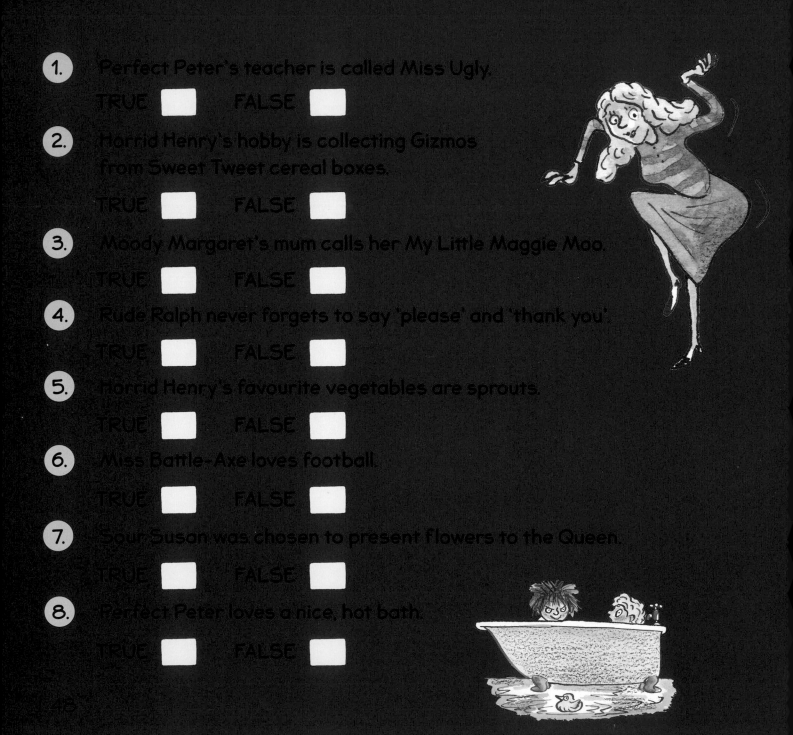

9. Perfect Peter's favourite book is called The Happy Nappy.

TRUE ☐ FALSE ☐

10. Horrid Henry loves shopping for new clothes

TRUE ☐ FALSE ☐

11. Moody Margaret plays the cello.

TRUE ☐ FALSE ☐

12. Rude Ralph's top talent is burping.

TRUE ☐ FALSE ☐

13. Horrid Henry tricks Bossy Bill into dancing nude on Miss Battle-Axe's desk.

TRUE ☐ FALSE ☐

14. The school's swimming teacher is called Drippy Dave.

TRUE ☐ FALSE ☐

15. Henry sold Perfect Peter to Moody Margaret for 50p.

TRUE ☐ FALSE ☐

Check out the answers on page 61 and count up your score.

11–15:

Brilliant! You're a big brainbox like the quick-witted quizmaster!

6–10:

Not a bad score – but you should have scored MORE!

0–5:

That's bad! You've been bamboozled by Brainy Brian's brainbusters!

Searching for a Secret Hide-out ...

Follow the flow chart and find the *best* den for your club!

Start here

Would you like a den outside in the garden? — **yes** → Do you want to meet where grown-ups are close by? — **no** → Will you hold top secret meetings in your den?

Do you want to meet where grown-ups are close by? — **yes** → Do you have a little brother or sister to be your sentry?

Will you hold top secret meetings in your den? — **yes** (from Do you want a secret hide-out...); **no** → Do you need a special hiding place for your stash of biscuits and your special secret code book?

Would you like a den outside in the garden? — **no** → Are you brave enough to defend your den from rival raids?

Are you brave enough to defend your den from rival raids? — **yes** → Do you have a little brother or sister to be your sentry?

Do you have a little brother or sister to be your sentry? — **no** ← Do you want a secret hide-out to make stinkbombs and Dungeon drinks?

Do you want a secret hide-out to make stinkbombs and Dungeon drinks? — **yes** (from Do you need a special hiding place...)

Do you need a special hiding place for your stash of biscuits and your special secret code book? — **no** → Does your club's Lord High Excellent Majesty demand a throne?

Are you brave enough to defend your den from rival raids? — **no** → Do you want a cosy carpet on the floor of your club den?

Do you have a little brother or sister to be your sentry? — **yes** → Will you be flying a club flag?

Do you want a cosy carpet on the floor of your club den? — **yes** → Will you be flying a club flag?

Will you be flying a club flag? — **yes** → Would you like your den to be clean and tidy?

Do you want a secret hide-out to make stinkbombs and Dungeon drinks? — **yes** → Would you like your den to be clean and tidy?

Would you like your den to be clean and tidy? — **no** → Does your club's Lord High Excellent Majesty demand a throne?

Will you be flying a club flag? — **no** → Do you love camping?

Do you want a cosy carpet on the floor of your club den? — **no** → Do you love camping?

Would you like your den to be clean and tidy? — **yes** → Are you scared of the dark?

Does your club's Lord High Excellent Majesty demand a throne? — **yes** → Will your den be camouflaged, so no one can find it?

Do you love camping? — **no** → Are you scared of the dark?

Do you love camping? — **yes** → Would you enjoy decorating your den walls with an interesting vegetable chart?

Are you scared of the dark? — **no** ← Will your den be camouflaged, so no one can find it?

Will your den be camouflaged, so no one can find it? — **yes** → Do you need a lookout, armed with a goo-shooter, on top of your den?

Are you scared of the dark? — **no** → Will you invite lots of friends to sleepovers in your den?

Would you enjoy decorating your den walls with an interesting vegetable chart? — **no** → Will you invite lots of friends to sleepovers in your den?

Do you need a lookout, armed with a goo-shooter, on top of your den? — **no** → Will you invite lots of friends to sleepovers in your den?

Would you enjoy decorating your den walls with an interesting vegetable chart? — **yes** → **Like Perfect Peter and his Best Boys club, your den should be tidy, clean and somewhere safe. Your BEDROOM would be perfect!**

Will you invite lots of friends to sleepovers in your den? — **yes** → **Like Moody Margaret and her Secret Club, you'd like somewhere big enough to fit all your friends, and a hidey hole for your secret stash of biscuits. A tent in the garden would be brilliant!**

Do you need a lookout, armed with a goo-shooter, on top of your den? — **yes** → **Like Horrid Henry and his Purple Hand Gang, you have to protect your den at all times from your arch-enemies. A top secret fort hidden away in the back garden of your house would be fantastic!**

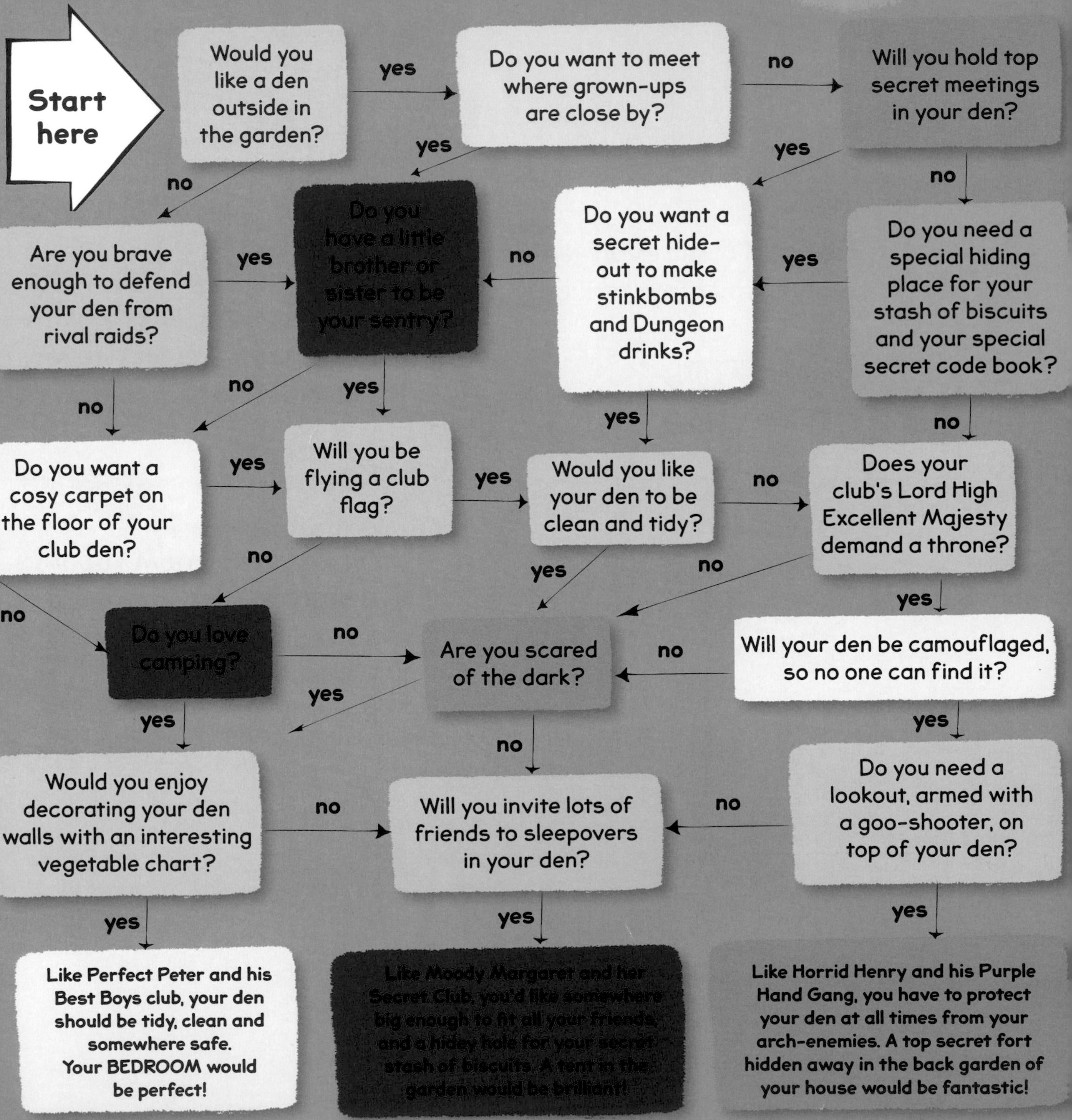

HORRID HENRY'S Raid

Horrid Henry watched and waited until it was dark and he heard the plinky-plonk sound of Moody Margaret practising her piano.

The coast was clear. Horrid Henry sneaked outside, jumped over the wall and darted inside the Secret Club Tent.

Swoop! He swept up the Secret Club pencils and secret code book.

Snatch! He snaffled the Secret Club stool.

Grab! He bagged the Secret Club biscuit tin.

Was that everything?

No!

Scoop! He snatched the Secret Club motto ('Down with boys').

Pounce! He pinched the Secret Club carpet.

Horrid Henry looked around. The Secret Club tent was bare.

Except for—

Henry considered. Should he?

Yes!

Whisk! The Secret Club tent collapsed. Henry gathered it into his arms with the rest of his spoils.

Huffing and puffing, gasping and panting, Horrid Henry staggered off over the wall, laden with the Secret Club. Raiding was hot, heavy work, but a pirate had to do his duty. Wouldn't all this booty look great decorating his fort? A rug on the floor, an extra biscuit tin, a repainted motto – 'Down with girls' – yes, the Purple Hand Fort would have to be renamed the Purple Hand Palace.

Speaking of which, where was the Purple Hand Fort?

Horrid Henry looked about wildly for the Fort entrance.

It was gone.

He searched for the Purple Hand throne.

It was gone.

And the Purple Hand biscuit tin – GONE!

There was a rustling sound in the shadows. Horrid Henry turned and saw a strange sight.

What does Horrid Henry see in the shadows? Find out in 'Horrid Henry's Raid' from *Horrid Henry and the Bogey Babysitter*.

Purple Hand Jokes Double Puzzle

Match the words to the Purple Hand Gang's favourite jokes and complete the punchlines.

3 letters	4 letters	5 letters	6 letters	8 letters
moo	head	grape	carrot	nostrils
	nose	smell	pooper	
		boots		

1. What's purple and sounds like an ape?
A _ _ _ _ _.

2. What do you get if you sit under a cow?
A pat on the _ _ _ _.

3. Why do giraffes have long necks?
Because their feet _ _ _ _ _.

4. How do you catch a rabbit?
Hide behind a tree and make a noise like a _ _ _ _ _ _.

5. Why do gorillas have big fingers?
Because they have big _ _ _ _ _ _ _ _.

6. Why didn't the centipede get picked for the football team?
It took him hours to get his _ _ _ _ _ on.

7. How do you stop a skunk smelling?
Hold his _ _ _ _.

8. Why did Peter take toilet paper to the party?
Because he was a party __ __ __ __ __ __.

9. What do you say to a cow on its birthday?
Happy birthday to __ __ __.

Now see if you can fit the same words into the criss-cross puzzle too.

TOP TIP:
Fill in the longest word first!

The answers are on page 61.

Skull and Crossbones Maze

Follow the smiling skull and crossbones to find the treasure. If you reach a dagger, you've taken the wrong path!

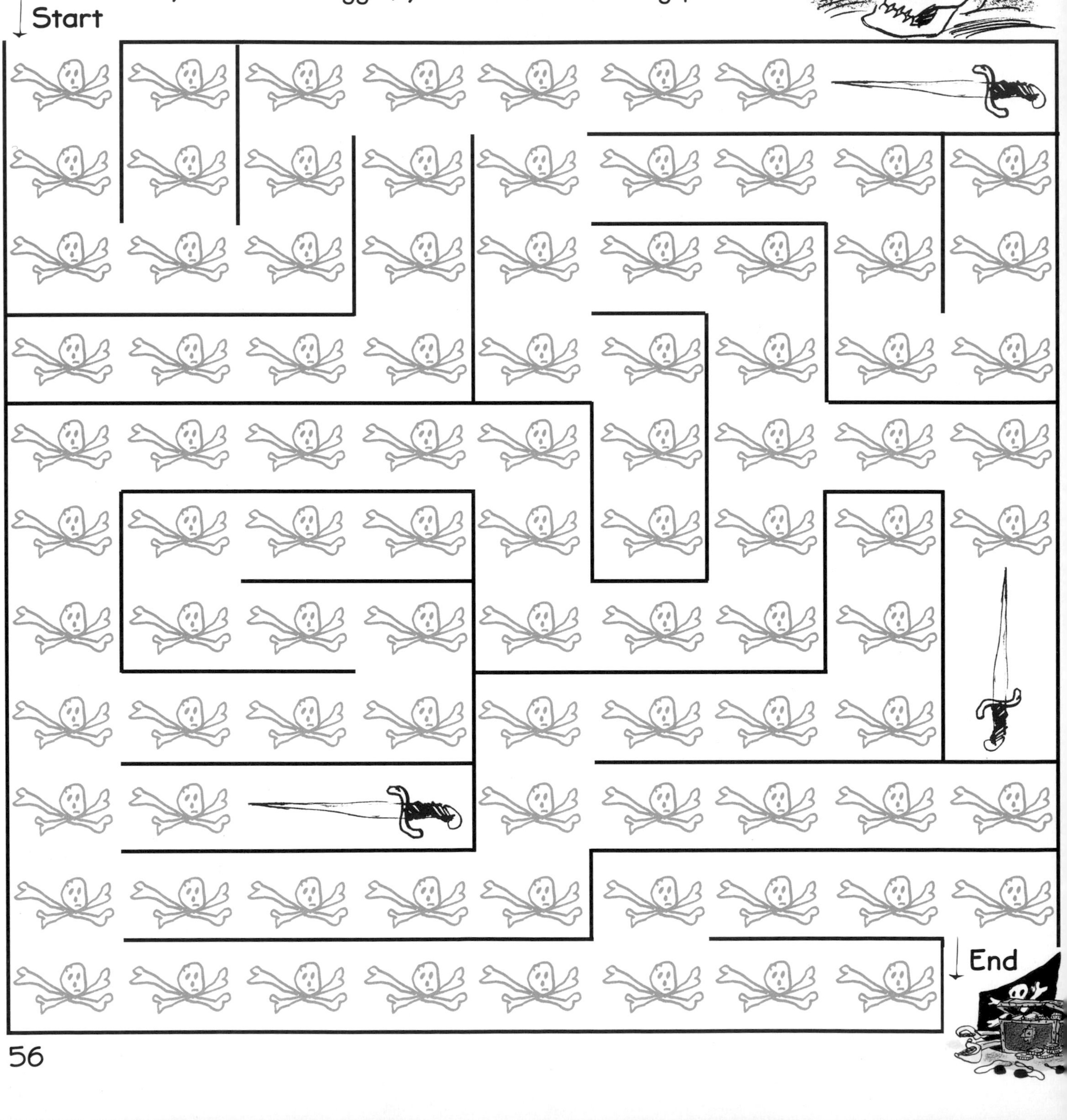

See you next year!

ANSWERS

Page 11

There are 19 Purple Hand prints on pages 9, 11, 14, 15, 22, 26, 27, 30, 31, 35, 39 (2 hands), 42 (2 hands), 44, 47, 50, 51 and 53.

Page 16

d	c	e	e	a	g	s	d	f	s
f	i	o	s	n	w	a	i	h	p
a	s	n	m	e	o	z	l	c	a
m	d	t	e	i	z	r	r	f	r
f	o	t	i	y	c	i	h	e	t
o	s	t	w	u	s	s	d	t	r
r	o	i	t	p	c	o	t	t	e
t	z	n	s	o	c	s	e	g	g
z	b	m	o	b	k	n	i	t	s
p	a	s	s	w	o	r	d	b	s

The leftover letters spell out:
dead fish and rotten eggs.

Page 19

1. a **2. d** **3. b** **4. c** **5. a**

Pages 22-23

1. It's **Horrid Henry's** birthday party.
2. Beefy Bert is playing **Pin the Tail on the Donkey**.
3. **Horrid Henry** is holding the Supersoaker Water Blaster 2000.
4. Greedy Graham is eating **chocolate cake**.
5. Anxious Andrew is hiding **under the table**.
6. **Yes!** Weepy William is crying in the picture.
7. **Sandwiches and cake**.
8. Horrid Henry is standing on a **chair**.
9. **Lazy Linda** and **Aerobic Al**.

Page 24

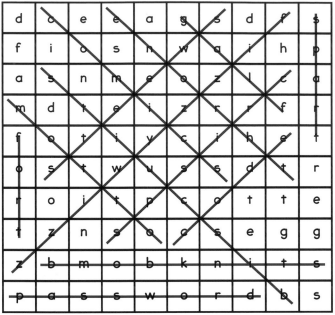

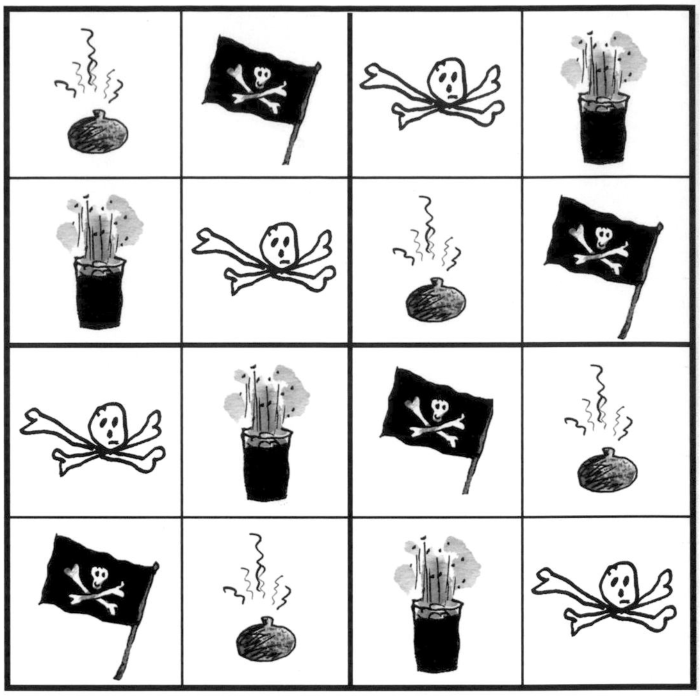

2	1	5	3	6	4
4	6	3	1	2	5
1	3	6	5	4	2
5	2	4	6	3	1
3	5	2	4	1	6
6	4	1	2	5	3

Page 25

		1 s					
	2 c	a	k	e	3 s		4 p
		n			l		a
5 b	e	d			e		n
a				6 m	e	a	t
7 b	o	o	8 m		p		s
y			a				
	9 f	a	n	g			

Page 26

Peter's code to Henry says:

Top secret spy report
A stash of chocolate has been hidden in the secret club tent.

Henry's code to Ralph says:

Urgent! Club grub raid today!
Meet at the fort after school.

Page 27

Peter's code to Margaret says:

Warning! The Purple Hand will raid tonight.

Margaret's code to Susan says:

Quick! Swap our chocolate with the mark of the dagger. Peter is Chief Spy now, not you.

Susan's code to Margaret says:

OK bossyboots!
The chocolate was yummy.
Nah nah ne nah nah.

Page 28

				h								
				a								
		c	u	t	l	a	s	s				
		r					w					
	h	o	o	k			o				e	
		s					r				y	
		s					d	a	g	g	e	r
s	a	b	r	e							p	
		o									a	
		n					c	h	e	s	t	
		e									c	
		s	k	u	l	l					h	

Page 29

Moody Margaret FLAG 13
Sour Susan FLAG 21
Lazy Linda FLAG 5
Singing Soraya FLAG 19
Gorgeous Gurinder FLAG 7

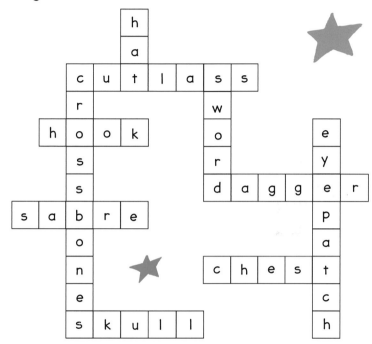

Page 34-35

Page 41

t	s	r	s	m	f	p	p	z	e
r	g	e	l	l	a	a	o	o	l
u	o	g	l	n	n	n	o	m	n
m	t	g	a	e	g	c	p	b	o
p	c	a	b	h	m	a	s	i	t
e	h	d	t	s	a	k	i	e	e
t	a	y	i	a	n	e	c	s	l
b	u	r	p	b	g	s	l	t	e
o	a	d	s	s	l	n	e	u	k
p	u	h	c	t	e	k	n	g	s
s	p	i	d	e	r	s	a	n	u

The Purple Hand password is: **smelly toads.**
The Secret Club password is: **nunga nu.**

Page 43

1st is: the Best Boys.
2nd is: the Purple Hand Gang.
3rd is: the Secret Club.

Page 47

	1 r	a	l	2 p	h		
				i			
3 p	e	4 t	e	r			5 t
i		i		a			r
n		e		t			a
k			6 h	e	n	7 r	y
						e	
		8 s	w	o	r	d	

Page 48-49

1. FALSE – She's called Miss Lovely.
2. TRUE
3. TRUE
4. FALSE – Rude Ralph always forgets!
5. FALSE – Horrid Henry hates ALL vegetables.
6. TRUE
7. FALSE – Perfect Peter was chosen to present flowers to the Queen.
8. FALSE – Perfect Peter likes his bath water cold and Horrid Henry likes his hot.
9. TRUE
10. FALSE
11. FALSE – Moody Margaret plays the trumpet.
12. TRUE
13. FALSE – Horrid Henry doesn't trick Bossy Bill into dancing nude on Miss Battle-Axe's desk – but he thinks it would be a very good idea to get Bill expelled from school!
14. FALSE – He's called Soggy Sid.
15. TRUE

Page 54-55

1. grape	4. carrot	7. nose
2. hcad	5. nostrils	8. pooper
3. smell	6. boots	9. moo

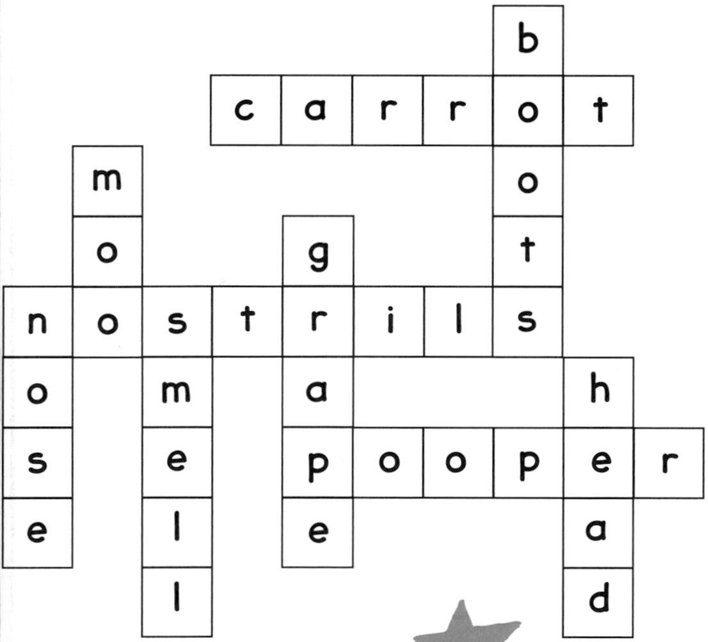

Page 56

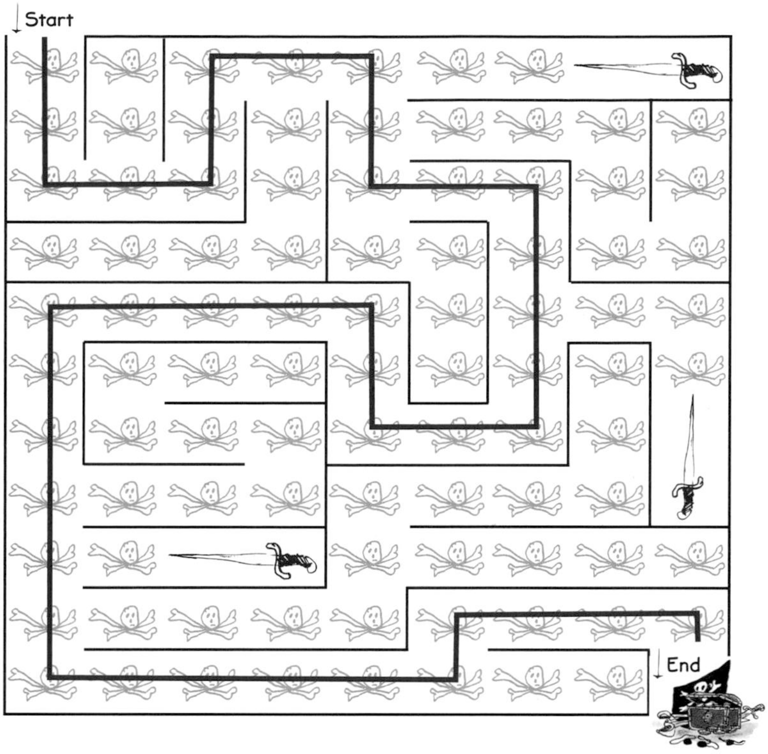